My Cat Can

by Gail Tuchman and Anne Schreiber
Illustrated by Tony Griego

SCHOLASTIC

Where can Cat run?

Cat can run to the can.

My cat can.

Where can Cat run?

Cat can run to the cup.

My cat can.

Where can Cat run?

Cat can run to the cap.

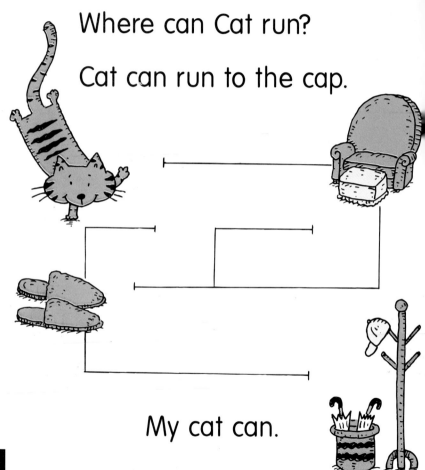

My cat can.

Where can Cat run?

Cat can run up, up, up to the top.

My cat can.

Where can Cat run?

Cat can run to my lap.

My cat can.

Cat can nap on my lap.

My cat can.

My Words

* cup

* run

lap

nap

on

top

Cc (/k/c)

can

cap

cat

*new high frequency words